Ladybird  Readers

The Magic Show

To access the audio and digital versions
of this book:

1 Go to **www.ladybirdeducation.co.uk**
2 Click "Unlock book"
3 Enter the code below

m1CgCJLxoX

Notes to teachers, parents, and carers

The *Ladybird Readers* Beginner level helps young language learners to become familiar with key conversational phrases in English. The language introduced has clear real-life applications, giving children the tools to hold their first conversations in English.

This book focuses on giving the instruction "Look!" and provides practice of saying prepositions of place, such as "on", "in", and "under", in English. The pictures that accompany the text show a classroom setting, which may be used to introduce one or two pieces of topic-based vocabulary, such as "chair" and "sit", if the children are ready.

There are some activities to do in this book. They will help children practice these skills:

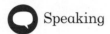 Speaking  Listening* Writing Reading Singing*

*To complete these activities, listen to the audio downloads available at **www.ladybirdeducation.co.uk**

Aardman

Series Editor: Sorrel Pitts   Text adapted by Hazel Geatches   Song lyrics by Wardour Studios

LADYBIRD BOOKS

UK | USA | Canada | Ireland | Australia
India | New Zealand | South Africa

Ladybird Books is part of the Penguin Random House group of companies whose addresses can be found at global.penguinrandomhouse.com.
www.penguin.co.uk   www.puffin.co.uk   www.ladybird.co.uk

Penguin
Random House
UK

First published 2021
001

This book is based on 'Learning Time with Timmy', an English language learning experience for pre-school children including the 'Learning Time with Timmy' courses
© British Council 2015; and the 'Learning Time with Timmy' series © Aardman Animations Ltd 2018.

'Timmy Time' and the character 'Timmy' are trademarks used under licence from Aardman Animations Limited.
'Learning Time with Timmy' is a trademark used under licence from Aardman Animations Limited.
britishcouncil.org/english/timmy

Printed in China
A CIP catalogue record for this book is available from the British Library
ISBN: 978-0-241-44001-8

All correspondence to:
Ladybird Books
Penguin Random House Children's
One Embassy Gardens, 8 Viaduct Gardens, London SW11 7BW

Ladybird 🐞 Readers

The Magic Show

Based on the Learning Time with Timmy TV series
created in partnership with the British Council

Watch the original episode "Show Time" online.

LEARN MORE!

Watch on ▶ YouTube

YouTube /LearningTimeWithTimmy
LearningTimeWithTimmy.com

Picture words

Timmy

Osbourne

Timmy's friends

magic show

box

pot

teddy bear

hat

Timmy and Osbourne
do a magic show.

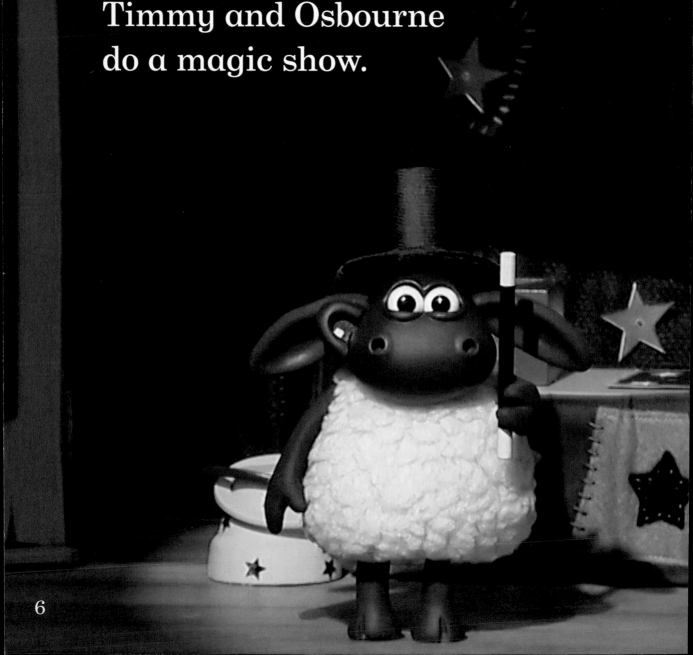

Timmy's friends watch the show.

There is a box on the table.

Timmy puts a pot on the box.
What is under the pot?

Look!
There is a teddy bear under
the pot!

Then, Timmy puts a hat on the table.

14

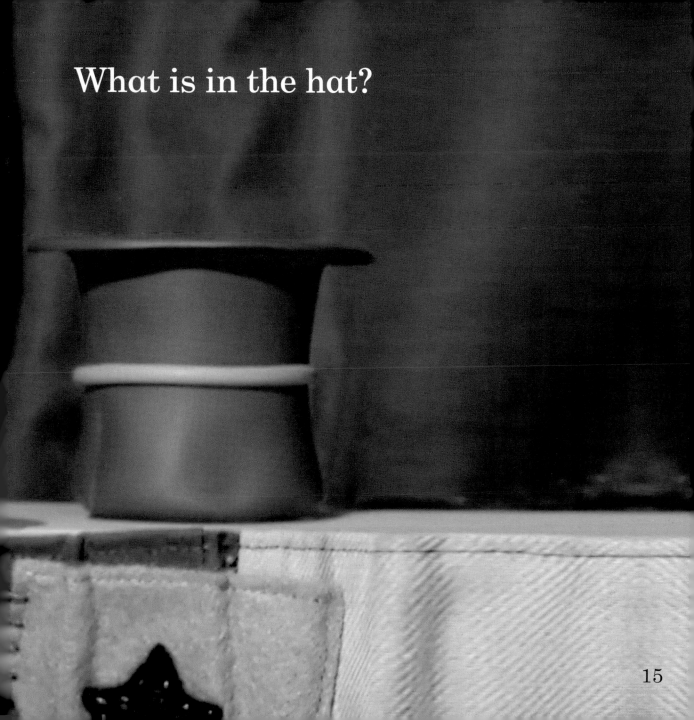

What is in the hat?

Look!
There are flowers in the hat!

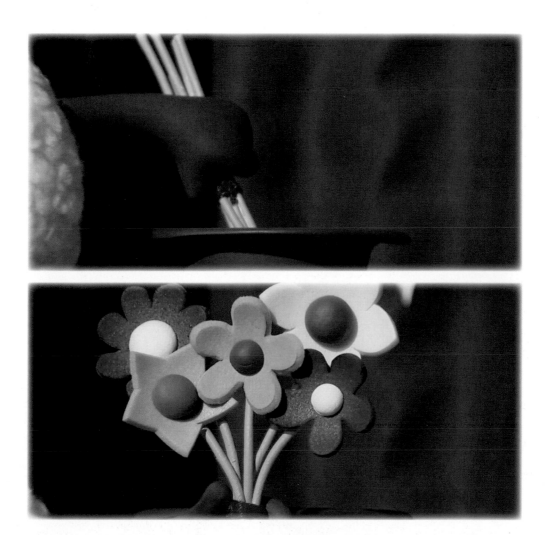

Timmy's friends love the
magic show.

Well done, Timmy and Osbourne!

Your turn!

1 **Talk with a friend.** 🗨

Where is the box?

It is on the table.

Where is the teddy bear?

It is under the pot.

2 Listen and read. Match. 🎧 📖

1 There is a teddy
bear under the pot.

2 There are flowers in
the hat.

3 There is a hat on
the table.

4 There is a pot on
the box.

3 What color? Listen. Circle the words.

1      (blue and red)   green and red

2      red   yellow

3      brown   blue

4      black   red

4 Listen. Write the first letters. 🎧 ✏️

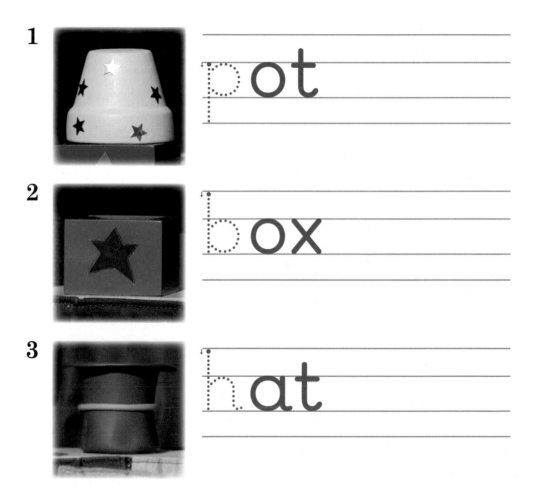

1 **p**ot

2 **b**ox

3 **h**at

5 Sing the song. 🎵

Magic, magic, magic show, magic, magic show.
Timmy's friends watch the magic show, magic, magic show.

Look! There is a box on the table!
Look! There is a pot on the box!
Look! There is a teddy bear under the pot!
Look! Look! Look!
Magic, magic, magic show, magic, magic show.
Timmy's friends watch the magic show, magic, magic show.

Look! There is a hat on the table!
Look! There are flowers in the hat!
Look! Timmy's friends love the magic show!
Look! Look! Look!